C000139645

The
Charles Dickens
Quiz
Book

Helen Barton

First Published 2000
© Helen Barton 2000

All rights reserved.
No reproduction permitted
without prior permission.

ISBN 0-9527257-3-8

Published by Helen Barton.
Printed by Aspect Design

For my family

CONTENTS

CHARLES DICKENS AND HIS FAMILY

1. When was Charles Dickens born?

2. How many brothers and sisters did he have?

3. Dickens was born in Chatham. True or false?

4. Which of the following books remained unfinished at his death:
   a) "Bleak House"   b) "The Mystery of Edwin Drood"
   c) "Dombey and Son"?

5. Dickens' father, John, was arrested. Why?

6. What was Charles Dickens' first job?

7. At what age did he go to school?

8. Dickens worked as a reporter. True or false?

9. Dickens used the pseudonym of "Boz" but can you explain why he chose it?

10. What was the name of his wife? Was it:
    a) Ellen   b) Maria   c) Catherine?

11. How many children did Dickens and his wife have?
    a) 10   b) 5   c) 8

12. George Hogarth was related to Dickens but in what way?

13. Dickens lived in Kent but can you name his house?

14. In 1833, Dickens had his first story published.
    What is it called?

15. The following are quotes from two prefaces but can you identify the books?

    a) "In all my writings, I hope I have taken every available opportunity of showing the want of sanitary improvements in the neglected dwellings of the poor."

    b) "I shall cherish the hope that every volume of this edition will afford me an opportunity of recording the extermination of some wrong or abuse set forth in it."

16. "Hard Times" is concerned with social problems of the Industrial Revolution.
    True or false?

17. In 1829, with whom did Dickens fall in love?

18. Do you know the novel Dickens first wrote under his own name?

19. Dickens and his wife separated.
    True or false?

20 On which member of the Dickens family is Micawber based?

21. "A Tale of Two Cities" and "Great Expectations" were serialised in "All the Year Round".
    True or false?

22. In 1850, Dickens founded a weekly magazine but what was it called?

23. After the birth of her ninth child, Catherine had a breakdown. Where did she go to recuperate?

24. In 1855 with whom did Dickens tour Italy and Switzerland?

25. Who was Ellen Ternan?

26. Dickens had a sister-in-law of whom he was very fond. What was her name?

27. What happened to her?

28. Who wrote "The Frozen Deep" and what was Dickens' involvement with it?

29. "The Signalman" and "To be Read at Dusk" are short stories but which type?

30. Name the book dedicated to Miss Burdett Coutts.

31. In which year did Dickens first visit America?

32. Whilst there, Dickens was criticised by the American press. Why?

33. George Cruikshank and "Sketches by Boz" are connected but in what way?

34. On whom is "Little Dorrit" based?

35. Where and when did Dickens die?

36. Do you know where he is buried?

NAME THE BOOK

1. Which book opens with the following lines:
   "Whether I shall turn out to be the hero of my own life, or whether that station will be held by anybody else, these pages must show."?

2. Match the following characters to the books in which they are found:

   i)   Magwitch   a) "A Christmas Carol"
   ii) Nancy   b) "Great Expectations"
   iii) Ebenezer Scrooge   c) "Oliver Twist"

3. Name as many books as you can which are named after a character in them.

4. Charles Dickens said:

   "Of all my books, I like this the best." Which one is it?

5. Where would you find:

   a) Fagin and Bill Sikes
   b) Pip and Miss Havisham?

6. Complete these titles:

   a) "Little . . . ."
   b) "The Mystery of. . . . ."
   c) "A Tale of. . . . ."

7. Which is Dickens' last completed book? Is it:

   a) "The Old Curiosity Shop"
   b) "Oliver Twist"
   c) "Our Mutual Friend" ?

8. "'It is a far, far better thing that I do, than I have ever done; it is a far, far better rest that I go to than I have ever known.'"
   Which novel closes with these lines?

9. Uriah Heep and Peggotty are characters from the same book but which one is it?

10. Where would you find :
    a) Little Nell
    b) Mrs. Gamp?

11. "Little Dorrit" is divided into three parts:
    "Book The First. Sowing."
    "Book The Second. Reaping."
    "Book The Third. Garnering."
    True or false?

12. Which of Dickens books is set during the French Revolution?

13. Where would you find the ghost of Jacob Marley?

14. Complete these titles:

    a) "Barnaby . . . ."
    b) "Nicholas . . . ."
    c) "Martin . . . ."

15. Winkle, Snodgrass and Tupman are all characters from "The Pickwick Papers." True or false?

16. Which is Dickens' first historical novel?

17. "A Christmas Carol" is one of three books which make up "The Christmas Books". Can you name either of the other two?

18. Swiveller and Quilp are both found in "The Old Curiosity Shop".
    True or false?

19. "Miss Flite, a little half-crazed old woman, a Suitor in Chancery" and "Mr. Turveydrop, a very gentlemanly man, celebrated for deportment" are both from the same novel Which one is it?

20. "The best story I have written". Which book is Dickens referring to? Is it:

    a) "Little Dorrit"
    b) "Bleak House"
    c) "A Tale of Two Cities"?

21. Name the book which opens with these lines:
    "Marley was dead, to begin with. There is no doubt whatever about that."?

22. Complete these titles:

    a) " . . . . House"
    b) " . . . . Times"
    c) " . . . . Friend"

23. Match these characters to the books in which they are found:

    a) Miss. Knag   i)   "The Mystery of Edwin Drood"
    b) Mrs. Blackpool   ii) "Nicholas Nickleby"
    c) Miss. Twinkleton iii) "Hard Times"

24 "Town and Todgers's" is a chapter from "Our Mutual Friend".
    True or False?

25. "Thirty years ago, Marseilles lay burning in the sun, one
    day." Are these the opening lines from "Little Dorrit" or
    "Hard Times"?

26. Florence, Harriet Carker and Edith are all found in the
    same novel but which one is it.
    Is it:

    a) "Barnaby Rudge"
    b) "Dombey and Son"
    c) "Martin Chuzzlewit"?

27. "Such are the changes which a few years bring about, and so
    do things pass away, like a tale that is told!"
    Name the book which closes with these lines.

28. Can you match these characters to the books in which
    they are found:

    a) Samuel Weller   i)   "A Christmas Carol"
    b) Bob Cratchit   ii) "The Pickwick Papers"
    c) Arthur Clennam   iii) "Little Dorrit"

29. Where would you find Tiny Tim?

30. Which book opens with these lines:
    "It was the best of times, it was the worst of times,
    it was the age of wisdom, it was the age of foolishness,"?

31. Emma Haredale and Edward Chester are characters from
    which novel?

32. "The American portion of this story is in no other respect a caricature,"
    Which of Dickens' books is he referring to?

33. "Allow me to introduce myself-first negatively."
    This is the opening line from "The Uncommercial Traveller."
    True or false?

34. "They comprise my first attempts at authorship".
    What are they?

NAME THE CHARACTER

1. "A fearful man, all in coarse gray, with a great iron on his leg." Who is this?

2. Name the character described in the following lines:
    "I saw that the bride within the bridal dress had withered like the dress, and like the flowers, and had no brightness left but the brightness of her sunken eyes."

3. Who says: "'Please, sir, I want some more.'" ?

4. Name the hero of "A Tale of Two Cities".

5. Match these characters to the books in which they are found:

    a) Little Em'ly   i)   "Oliver Twist"
    b) Rose Fleming   ii) "Great Expectations"
    c) Estella   iii) "David Copperfield"

6. What is Mr. Pickwick's first name?

7. "He was a snub-nosed, flat-browed, common-faced boy enough; and as dirty a juvenile as one would wish to see; but he had about him all the airs and manners of a man. He was short of his age: with rather bow-legs, and little, sharp, ugly eyes." Who is he?

8. Can you identify the following two characters?
    "X was about eight-and-forty years of age. Son about eight-and-forty minutes."

9. Which character from "The Old Curiosity Shop" is described in the following lines: "His black eyes were restless, sly, and cunning; his mouth and chin, bristly with the stubble of a coarse hard beard; and his complexion was one of that kind which never looks clean or wholesome. But what added most to the grotesque expression of his face, was a ghastly smile."?

10. A character called Amy is born in Marshalsea Prison but how is she better known?

11. "'Oh, believe me, no! Such a thought never came into my head! I shouldn't have deemed it at all proud if you had thought *us* too umble for you. Because we are so very umble.'"
Who is speaking?

12. In "Great Expectations" which character washes his hands obsessively?

13. Newman Noggs and Mr. Vincent Crummles are characters in "Hard Times".
True or false?

14. Which character has a red birthmark?

15. Mrs. Gamp is found in "Martin Chuzzlewit" but what is her first name? Is it:

    a) Sarah   b) Mercy   c) Charity ?

16. Match the characters to the books in which they are found:

    a) Dr. Strong   i) "Oliver Twist"
    b) The Artful Dodger ii) "Hard Times"
    c) Josephine Sleary   iii) "David Copperfield"

17. The following characters are all from "A Christmas Carol" but can you complete their names?
    a) Jacob . . . .
    b) Ebenezer . . . .
    c) Bob . . . .

18. Who in "Hard Times" is "a mysterious old woman, withered, but tall and shapely."?

19. "The general supposition was that he had committed suicide, and, this appearing to be favoured by all the circumstances of his death, the verdict was to that effect. He was left to be buried with a stake through his heart in the centre of four lonely roads."
    These lines refer to Quilp in "The Old Curiosity Shop."
    True or false?

20. In "Barnaby Rudge" who or what is Grip?

21. The following is from "Our Mutual Friend" but can you name the characters:

    a) "forty, wavy haired, dark, tending to corpulence, sly, mysterious, filmy";

    b) "Sooth to say, he was so wooden a man that he seemed to have taken his wooden leg naturally."?

22. Lucie and Madame Defarge are characters from "A Tale of Two Cities".
    True or false?

23. The following is from "The Pickwick Papers" but can you name the characters:

    a) "a casual observer might possibly have remarked nothing extraordinary in the bald head and circular spectacles which were intently turned towards his (the secretary's) face during the reading of the above resolutions;"

b) "It is very possible that at some earlier period of his career Mr. X's profile might have presented a bold and determined outline. His face, however, had expanded under the influence of good living."

24. Who in "The Mystery of Edwin Drood" had "grown to be an amiable, giddy, wilful, winning little creature;"?

25. "a handsome, but headstrong and passionate girl; maid to Miss Minnie Meagles."
This character is found in "Little Dorrit" but who is she?

26. The following describes a character from "Dombey and Son" but can you identify her?
"She had the softest voice that ever was heard; and her nose, stupendously aquiline, had a little knob in the very centre or key-stone of the bridge, whence it tended downwards towards her face, as in an invincible determination never to turn up at anything."

27. Who had "a large bundle with her, a pair of pattens, and a species of gig umbrella;" and whose face "was somewhat red and swollen, and it was difficult to enjoy her society without becoming conscious of a smell of spirits." ?

1. Which book is set in London and in Paris?

2. "The marsh country, down by the river" is the opening setting of which novel?

3. Marshalsea Prison appears in which book? Is it:
   a) "Little Dorrit"
   b) "The Mystery of Edwin Drood"
   c) "Our Mutual Friend"?

4. "The room in which the boys were fed, was a large stone hall, with a copper at one end: out of which the master, dressed in an apron for the purpose, and assisted by one or two women, ladled the gruel at meal-times."
   Name the book from which these lines are taken.

5. Where would you find the town of Cloisterham?

6. Who is born at Blunderstone? Is it:

   a) Oliver Twist
   b) David Copperfield
   c) Barnaby Rudge?

7. "Certain wintry branches of candles on the high chimney-piece faintly lighted the chamber: or, it would be more expressive to say, faintly troubled its darkness. It was spacious, and I daresay had once been handsome, but every discernible thing in it was covered with dust and mould, and dropping to pieces."
   Whose house is this?

8. "Bell Yard" and "Down in Lincolnshire" are two chapter headings but where are they found? Is it:
   a) "Barnaby Rudge"
   b) "Bleak House"
   c) "Hard Times"?

9. In which book would you find Coketown?

10. The following are three descriptions of London but can you name the novels from which they are taken?

   a) "Covent Garden market at sunrise too, in the spring or summer, when the fragrance of sweet flowers is in the air, overpowering even the unwholesome streams of last night's debauchery, and driving the dusky thrush, whose cage has hung outside a garret window all night long, half mad with joy!"

   b) "London. Michaelmas Term lately over, and the Lord Chancellor sitting in Lincoln's Inn Hall. Implacable November weather. As much mud in the streets, as if the waters had but newly retired from the face of the earth, and it would not be wonderful to meet a Megalosaurus, forty feet long or so, waddling like an elephantine lizard up Holborn Hill."

   c) "but I know that I was often up at six o'clock, and that my favourite lounging-place in the interval was old London Bridge, where I was wont to sit in one of the stone recesses, watching the people going by, or to look over the balustrades at the sun shining in the water, and lighting up the golden flame on the top of the Monument."

11. Who lives at Satis House?

12. "If it had been Aladdin's palace, roc's egg and all, I suppose I could not have been more charmed with the romantic idea of living in it. There was a delightful door cut in the side, and it was roofed in, and there were little windows in it; but the wonderful charm of it was, that it was a real boat which had no doubt been upon the water hundreds of times, and which had never been intended to be lived in, on dry land." Can you name the book?

13. Which book is partly set in America?

14. Where would you find Dotheboys Hall?

15. Which novel has as a setting the Gordon riots of 1780? Is it:
    a) "Bleak House"
    b) "David Copperfield"
    c) "Barnaby Rudge"?

16. "An Ancient English cathedral tower? How can the ancient English cathedral tower be here? The well-known massive grey square tower of its old cathedral? How can that be here?"
    Name the novel which opens with these lines.

17. The Salem House Academy is found in "Dombey and Son". True or false?

18. Yorkshire is a setting in which novel? Is it:

    a) "Oliver Twist"
    b) "Nicholas Nickleby"
    c) "Martin Chuzzlewit"?

19. In which of the novels would you find "a house of public entertainment called the Maypole"?

20. "There were suits of mail standing like ghosts in armour, here and there; fantastic carvings brought from monkish cloisters; rusty weapons of various kinds - distorted figures in china, and wood, and iron, and ivory; tapestry, and strange furniture that might have been designed in dreams."
    This is from "The Old Curiosity Shop". True or false?

21. Where would you find the following Chapter Heading: "Accompanies Mr. Pecksniff and his charming Daughters to the City of London; and relates what fell out, upon their way thither,"?

22. "There was no house now, no brewery, no building whatever left, but the wall of the old garden. The cleared space had been enclosed with a rough fence, and, looking over it, I saw that some of the old ivy had struck root anew and was growing green on low quiet mounds of ruin."
    Where are these lines from?

23. When "Nicholas Nickleby" opens, the Nickleby family are living in Cornwall. True or false?

LOVE AND MARRIAGE

I.   In "Oliver Twist" who does Rose Fleming marry?

2.   David Copperfield marries twice. Can you name his wives?

3.   "And they were married, with the sun shining on them through the painted figure of Our Saviour on the window." Who are they?

4.   In "A Tale of Two Cities" who is Lucie's husband?

5.   "When her term of mourning had expired, Madeline gave her hand and fortune to Nicholas, and on the same day and at the same time Kate became Mrs. Frank Cheeryble." Where are these lines from?

6.   Who does Edward Chester marry in "Barnaby Rudge"?

7.   Who dresses permanently as a bride?

8.   Which bride has a letter delivered to her on her wedding morning and after reading it "uttered a piercing shriek; threw it down upon the ground; and fainted away." ?

9.   Joe Gargery ("Great Expectations") remarries at the end of the novel but to whom?

10. Match these couples from Bleak House:

    a) Allan   i) Esther
    b) Richard   ii) Ada

11. "Meanwhile the marriage was appointed to be solemnized in eight weeks' time, and Mr. Bounderby went every evening to Stone Lodge, as an accepted wooer. Love was made on these occasions in the form of bracelets; and, on all occasions during the period of betrothal, took a manufacturing aspect."
Where is this from?

12. Who is described as " a lover of Little Dorrit"?

13. "The betrothal of Rosa grew out of the soothing of his year of mental distress by his fast friend and old college companion," This is from "The Mystery of Edwin Drood". True or false?

14. "Did Kit live a single man all his days, or did he marry? Of course he married, and who should be his wife but Barbara?" Are these lines from:

    a) "The Old Curiosity Shop"
    b) "Nicholas Nickleby"
    c) "Martin Chuzzlewit"?

15. In which book do Bunsby and Mrs. MacStinger marry?

16. "It was not very long, as may be sure, before Joe Willet and Dolly Varden were made husband and wife,"
Are these lines from:

    a) "The Pickwick Papers"
    b) "Nicholas Nickleby"
    c) "Barnaby Rudge"?

17. The following is from "Nicholas Nickleby"
    but who is speaking:
    "we are too old to be single - why shouldn't we both be
    married instead of sitting through the long winter evenings
    by our solitary firesides? Why shouldn't we make one fireside
    of it, and marry each other?"

18. Who is Martin Chuzzlewit's "Lady of his Love"?

19. Name the book which has chapters entitled:
    "The Interval before the Marriage", "The Wedding" and
    "Chiefly Matrimonial."

20. "A wedding is a licensed subject to joke upon, but there
    really is no great joke in the matter after all;"
    This is from "Our Mutual Friend". True or false?

21. In which novel do a brother and sister marry on the same
    day as one another?

22. In "David Copperfield" who is Ham going to marry?

23. "'So that Mrs. Badger has been married to three husbands-
    two of them highly distinguished men', said Mr. Badger
    summing up the facts; 'and, each time, upon the twenty-first
    of March at Eleven in the forenoon!'"
    Is this from "Bleak House" or "Little Dorrit"?

24. In "Oliver Twist" who does Mr. Bumble marry?

25. Can you identify the characters from the following lines?
    "Once for all; I knew to my sorrow, often and often, if not
    always, that I loved her against reason, against promise,
    against peace, against hope, against happiness, against all
    discouragement that could be."

26. "Of my walking so proudly and lovingly down the aisle with my sweet wife upon my arm, through a mist of half-seen people, pulpits, monuments, pews, fonts, organs, and church windows, in which there flutter faint airs of association with my childish church at home, so long ago."
Whose wedding is this?

27. Mr. Brownlow ("Oliver Twist") was to have been married but to whom?

28. The following is from "The Pickwick Papers" but who is speaking: "'Take example by your father, my boy, and be wery careful o' widders all your life, especially if they've kept a public house, Sammy.'"

FAMILIES

1. In which book would you find the Cratchit family?

2. Who has an aunt called Betsey Trotwood?

3. In "Little Dorrit" William Dorrit has two daughers.
    Can you name them both?

4. What is the relationship between Oliver Twist and Rose
    Fleming?

5. Which relation of Nell has The Old Curiosity Shop?

6. In "David Copperfield" Mr. Wickfield has a daughter but
    what is she called? Is her name:

    a) Jane   b) Dora   c) Agnes?

7. Whose daughter is Estella?

8. "In the Mystery of Edwin Drood" what is the relationship
    between John Jasper and Edwin Drood?

9. Match the following families to the novels in which they are
    found

    a) The Micawber Family   i)   "Little Dorrit"
    b) The Barnacle Family   ii) "David Copperfield"
    c) The Gradgrind Family   iii) "Hard Times"

10. In which book would you find the Cheeryble brothers and
    the Squeers family?

11. Oliver Twist and David Copperfield both lose their parents.
    True or False?

12. Paul Dombey has a sister. Is her name:

    a) Edith   b) Harriet   c) Florence?

13. In "Bleak House" whose daughters are Malta and Quebec?

14. Where would you find the Peggotty family?

15. Nicholas Nickleby has a sister.
    True or false?

16. In "A Christmas Carol" whose sister is Fan?

17. What is the relationship in "Barnaby Rudge" between Reuben Haredale and Emma?

18. Who has a half-brother called Edward?

19. In "Little Dorrit" Bob is turnkey of the Marshalsea Prison but what is his relationship to Little Dorrit?

20. The Landless twins are found in "The Mystery of Edwin Drood". Can you name them?

21. "My aunt was a tall, hard-featured lady, but by no means ill looking." Where are these lines taken from?

22. Match these families to the books in which they are found:

    a) The Varden Family   i)   "A Christmas Carol"
    b) Mr. and Mrs. Fezziwigg ii) "Martin Chuzzlewit"
    c) Tom and Ruth Pinch   iii) "Barnaby Rudge"

23. "She was not a good-looking woman, my sister; and I had a general impression that she must have made Joe Gargery marry her by hand." Who is speaking?

24. In what way are Ralph and Kate Nickleby related?

25. In which book would you find Mercy and Charity Pecksniff?

26. "This baby was one of twins; and I may remark here that I hardly ever, in all my experience of the family, saw both the twins detached from Mrs. M… at the same time. One of them was always taking refreshment."
Who is Mrs. M?

27. Name the book where you would find the following:
"Mrs. Nupkins was a majestic female in a pink gauze turban and a light-brown wig. Miss Nupkins possessed all her mama's haughtiness without the turban, and all her ill-nature without the wig;"

28. The following lines are from "Great Expectations" but can you name the family?
"After dinner the children were introduced, and Mrs. Coiler made admiring comments on their eyes, noses, and legs – a sagacious way of improving their minds. There were four little girls, and two little boys, besides the baby who might have been either, and the baby's next successor who was as yet neither."

OLIVER TWIST

1. Where is Oliver Twist born?

2. How did he come by the name of "Twist"?

3. Who is described as "a fat man, and a choleric;"?

4. Mr. Brownlow has a housekeeper. Is she called:

    a) Mrs. Bates   b) Mrs. Bedwin   c) Mrs. Claypole

5. Match these characters to their professions:

    a) Mr. Sowerberry   i)   Doctor
    b) Mr. Fang   ii) Undertaker
    c) Mr. Losberne   iii) Magistrate

6. Name Oliver Twist's parents.

7. Old Sally is matron of the workhouse where Oliver Twist is
    born.
    True or false?

8. Match these characters correctly:

    a) Charley Bates   i)   friend of Mr. Brownlow's
    b) Mr. Grimwig   ii) pickpocket
    c) Duff   iii) policeman

9. What is Mr. Brownlow's relationship to Oliver's father?

10. "No chance-child was he, for he could trace his genealogy all
    the way back to his parents,"
    To whom do these lines refer?

11. Mr. Gamfield and Mr. Giles are butler and chimney sweep.
    But which is which?

12. "The old gentleman was a very respectable-looking personage, with a powdered head and gold spectacles."
Who is he?

13. What is the Artful Dodger's real name?

14. "They wore a good deal of hair, not very neatly turned up behind, and were rather untidy about the shoes and stockings. They were not exactly pretty, perhaps; but they had a great deal of colour in their faces, and looked quite stout and hearty."
Who are they?

15. Monks is related to Oliver but in what way?

16. Whose "villanous-looking and repulsive face was obscured by a quantity of matted red hair."?

17. What is Monks' real name?

18. "He disclosed... a broad heavy countenance with a beard of three days' growth, and two scowling eyes;"
Who is he?

19. What happens to Nancy?

20. "She was not past seventeen. Cast in so slight and exquisite a mould; so mild and gentle; so pure and beautiful; that earth seemed not her element, nor its rough creatures her fit companions." Can you identify her?

21. How is Mrs. Maylie related to Rose Fleming?

22. "Staggering as if struck by lightening, he lost his balance and tumbled over the parapet. The noose was on his neck. It ran up with his weight, tight as a bowstring, and swift as the arrow it speeds. He fell for five-and-thirty feet."
    Who is he?

23. Whose son is Harry?

24. "He grew so terrible, at last, in all the tortures of his evil conscience, that one man could not bear to sit there, eyeing him alone; and so the two kept watch together."
    This is Fagin. True or false?

25. At the end of the book, who adopts Oliver "as his son"?

GREAT EXPECTATIONS

1. What is Pip's full name and why is he known as Pip?

2. Who is Magwitch and where does he first meet Pip?

3. Can you name the people Pip lives with, as a child?

4. Mrs. Joe gives Pip and her husband a certain type of medicinal drink.
   What is it?

5. "She was dressed in rich materials - satins, and lace, and silks - all of white. Her shoes were white. And she had a long white veil dependent from her hair, and she had bridal flowers in her hair, but her hair was white."
   Who is she?

6. At what time have all the clocks at Satis House stopped?

7. "'I don't suffer it to be spoken of.'"
   To which day is Miss Havisham referring?

8. Joe Gargery is a blacksmith.
   True or false?

9. At Miss Havisham's house, Pip meets a young lady who is described as "very pretty and seemed very proud."
   What is her name?

10. Match the following characters correctly:

    a) Jaggers   i)   friend of Pip's
    b) Herbert Pocket   ii) Magwitch's ex partner in crime
    c) Compeyson   iii) a lawyer

11. What is Magwitch's first name?

12. 'Well! You can break his heart.'
    According to Pip, who think he overhears this, who is speaking and to whom?

13. "I checked off again in detail, his large head, his dark complexion, his deep-set eyes, his bushy black eyebrows, his large watch-chain, his strong black dots of beard and whisker, and even the smell of scented soap on his great hand."
    Who is he?

14. Who "professed to be Miss Havisham's lover" but abandoned her on her wedding day?

15. Pip has a secret benefactor. Can you name him?

16. What is Estella's relationship to Miss Havisham?

17. Name "the journeyman" kept by Joe Gargery.

18. What is his first name. Is it:

    a) Dolge   b) Herbert   c) Joe?

19. "The pale young gentleman and I stood contemplating one another in Barnard's Inn, until we both burst out laughing."
    Who is "the pale young gentleman"?

20. Where does Pip go to begin his new life as a gentleman?

21. Pip's sister is attacked but by whom?

22. Mr. Pumplechook is related to Joe Gargery but in what way?

23. "'I stole her heart away and put ice in its place.'"
    Can you identify the characters?

24. In which country did Magwitch make his money?

25. "'Now, wolf' said he, 'afore I kill you like any other beast-
    which is wot I mean to do and wot I have tied you up for-
    I'll have a good look at you and a good goad at you. Oh,
    you enemy!'"
    Who is speaking?

26. Estella marries someone called Drummle but what is
    his first name?

27. "In the same moment, I saw her running at me, shrieking,
    with a whirl of fire blazing all about her, and soaring at
    least as many feet above her head as she was high."
    Who is she?

28. Name the person who betrays Magwitch.

29. Three people go by boat to try and help Magwitch escape.
    Pip is one. Name the other two.

30. Who is Provis?

31. What happens to Magwitch?

32. "Many a year went round, before I was a partner in the
    House; but I lived happily … and lived frugally, and paid my
    debts, and maintained a constant correspondence with
    Biddy and Joe."
    Who is Pip living with at this time?

33. Where do Pip and Estella re-meet?

DAVID COPPERFIELD

1. Who is Peggotty?

2. David's mother is a widow.
   True or false?

3. "A squareness about the lower part of his face, and the dotted indication of the strong black beard he shaved close every day, reminded me of the wax-work that had travelled into our neighbourhood some half a year before."
   Who is this?

4. What is unusual about Mr. Peggotty's home?

5. Name the headmaster of Salem House Academy.

6. David makes two friends at Salem House.
   A point for each one you know

7. What is Mr. Micawber's first name?

8. Mr. Peggotty has adopted an "orphan nephew and niece".
   Who are they?

9. Where does Miss Betsey live? Is it:

   a) Dover   b) London   c) Canterbury ?

10. "'I'm a bacheldore'" and "'I am as rough as a Sea Porkypine;'"
    Who is speaking?

11. Whose school does David go to in Canterbury?

12. What is Mr. Wickfield's profession?

13. Agnes is Dr. Strong's daughter.
    True or false?

14. What are the first names of:

    a) Peggotty   b) Mr. Peggotty
    c) Traddles   d) Steerforth?

15. "He had a way of writhing when he wanted to express enthusiasm, which was very ugly; and which diverted my attention from the compliment he had paid my relation to the snaky twistings of his throat and body."
    Name the person described in these lines.

16. "His hair was quite white now, though his eyebrows were still black. He had a very agreeable face, and, I thought, was handsome."
    Who is he?

17. What is Uriah Heep's job?

18. Who says:" 'Umble we are, umble we have been, umble we shall ever be,"'?

19. David's aunt becomes one of his guardians.
    Who is the other?

20. "Trotwood" and "Daisy" are names which are given to David but by whom?

21. Who does Barkis marry?

22. "'It took place this here present hour; and here's the man that'll marry her, the minute she's out of her time'".
    This is Mr. Peggotty talking but who is he referring to?

23. Who does Little Em'ly run away with?

24. David Copperfield works in the firm of Spenlow and Jorkins but whose daughter does he fall in love with and what is her name?

25. Identify these three characters:

    a) 'a most beautiful little girl (or I thought her so) with a necklace of blue beads on, who wouldn't let me kiss her when I offered to, but ran away and hid herself'

    b) 'Although her face was quite bright and happy, there was a tranquillity about it, and about her - a quiet, good, calm spirit,- that I never have forgotten; that I never shall forget."

    c) "She was more than human to me. She was a Fairy, a Sylph, I don't know what she was - anything that no one ever saw, and everything that everybody ever wanted. I was swallowed up in an abyss of love in an instant."

26. What happens to Dora and to the child she has with David?

27. Ham and Steerforth are drowned.
    True or false?

28. 'Her chin, which was called a double-chin, was so fat that it entirely swallowed up the strings of her bonnet, bow and all. Throat she had none; waist she had none; legs she had none, worth mentioning;'
    Who is she?

29.   What is Tommy Traddles' profession? Is it:

a) legal

b) clerical?

30. "Fraud, forgery, and conspiracy - he and some others - he set the others on. It was a deep plot for a large sum. Sentence, transportation for life.".
To whom to these lines refer?

31. Mr. Peggotty, Little Em'ly and Mr. Micawber finally live abroad but where? Is it:

a) Australia

b) America ?

ANSWERS

ANSWERS: CHARLES DICKENS AND HIS FAMILY

1. 1812.

2. Seven.

3. False. Portsmouth.

4. b) "The Mystery of Edwin Drood".

5. For being in debt.

6. Labelling bottles in a warehouse.

7. Twelve.

8. True.

9. It was the nickname of a younger brother.

10. c) Catherine.

11. Ten.

12. Father-in-law.

13. Gad's Hill.

14. "A Dinner at Poplar Walk."

15. a) "Martin Chuzzlewit"

   b) "The Pickwick Papers"

16. True.

17. Maria Beadnell.

18. "Oliver Twist"

19. True.

20. John, his father.

21. True.

22. "Household Words".

23. Malvern.

24. Wilkie Collins.

25. An actress, with whom Dickens fell in love.

26. Mary Hogarth.

27. She died suddenly, aged seventeen.

28. Wilkie Collins. Dickens took the play to Manchester.

29. Ghost stories.

30. "Martin Chuzzlewit".

31. 1841.

ANSWERS: CHARLES DICKENS AND HIS FAMILY

32.   Dickens supported the abolition of slavery.

33.   Cruikshank was the illustrator.

34.   Georgina Hogarth, Dickens' sister-in-law.

35.   Gad's Hill, 1870.

36.   Poet's Corner, Westminster Abbey.

1. "David Copperfield."

2. Magwitch - "Great Expectations";

    Nancy - "Oliver Twist";

    Ebenezer Scrooge - "A Christmas Carol".

3. "David Copperfield", "Oliver Twist",

    "Little Dorrit", "Dombey and Son",

    "Barnaby Rudge", "Martin Chuzzlewit",

    "Nicholas Nickleby", "The Mystery of Edwin Drood",

    "The Pickwick Papers"

4. "David Copperfield".

5. a) "Oliver Twist"

    b) "Great Expectations".

6. "Little Dorrit";

    "The Mystery of Edwin Drood";

    "A Tale of Two Cities."

7. "Our Mutual Friend".

8. "A Tale of Two Cities".

9. "David Copperfield".

ANSWERS: NAME THE BOOK

10. Little Nell - "The Old Curiosity Shop".
    Mrs. Gamp - "Martin Chuzzlewit".

11. False. "Hard Times".

12. "A Tale of Two Cities".

13. "A Christmas Carol".

14. a) "Barnaby Rudge"
    b) "Nicholas Nickleby"
    c) "Martin Chuzzlewit"

15. True.

16. "Barnaby Rudge".

17. "The Chimes" and "The Cricket on the Hearth".

18. True.

19. "Bleak House".

20 "A Tale of Two Cities".

21. "A Christmas Carol".

22. a) "Bleak House"
    b) "Hard Times"
    c) "Our Mutual Friend"

23. Miss Knag - "Nicholas Nickleby";

    Mrs. Blackpool - "Hard Times";

    Miss Twinkleton - "The Mystery of Edwin Drood".

24. False. "Martin Chuzzlewit".

25. "Little Dorrit".

26. b) "Dombey and Son".

27. "The Old Curiosity Shop".

28. Samuel Weller   -   "The Pickwick Papers";

    Bob Cratchit   -   "A Christmas Carol";

    Arthur Clennam   -   "Little Dorrit".

29. "A Christmas Carol".

30. "A Tale of Two Cities".

31. "Barnaby Rudge".

32. "Martin Chuzzlewit".

33. True.

34. "Sketches by Boz".

ANSWERS: NAME THE CHARACTER

1. Magwitch.

2. Miss Havisham.

3. Oliver Twist.

4. Sydney Carton

5. Little Em'ly   -   "David Copperfield"
    Rose Fleming   -   "Oliver Twist"
    Estella   -   " Great Expectations"

6. Samuel.

7. The Artful Dodger.

8. Mr. Dombey and Paul Dombey

9. Quilp.

10. Little Dorrit.

11. Uriah Heep.

12. Jaggers.

13. False. Nicholas Nickleby.

14. Barnaby Rudge.

15. a) Sarah.

16. Dr. Strong   -   "David Copperfield"

     The Artful Dodger   -   "Oliver Twist"

     Josephine Sleary   -   "Hard Times"

17. Jacob Marley, Ebenezer Scrooge and Bob Cratchit

18. Mrs. Pegler

19. True.

20. A raven.

21. a) Mr. Veneering

     b) Silas Wegg

22. True.

23. a) Mr. Pickwick

     b) Samuel Weller

24. Rosa

25. Harriet Beadle ('Tattycoram')

26. Miss Tox

27. Mrs. Gamp.

1. "A Tale of Two Cities".

2. "Great Expectations".

3. a) "Little Dorrit".

4. "Oliver Twist".

5. "The Mystery of Edwin Drood".

6. b) David Copperfield.

7. Miss Havisham's.

8. b) "Bleak House".

9. "Hard Times".

10. a) "The Old Curiosity Shop";
    b) "Bleak House";
    c) "David Copperfield".

11. Miss Havisham.

12. "David Copperfield".

13. "Martin Chuzzlewit".

14. "Nicholas Nickleby".

15. c) "Barnaby Rudge".

16. "The Mystery of Edwin Drood".

17. False. "David Copperfield".

18. b) "Nicholas Nickleby".

19. "Barnaby Rudge".

20. True.

21. "Martin Chuzzlewit".

22. "Great Expectations".

23. False. Devonshire.

ANSWERS: LOVE AND MARRIAGE

I. Harry Maylie.

2. Dora and Agnes.

3. Arthur Clennam and Little Dorrit.

4. Charles Darnay.

5. "Nicholas Nickleby"

6. Emma.

7. Miss Havisham.

8. Miss Pecksmith ("Martin Chuzzlewit")

9. Biddy.

10. Richard and Ada, Allan and Esther.

11. "Hard Times".

12. Young John Chivery.

13. True.

14. a) "The Old Curiosity Shop".

15. "Dombey and Son".

16. c) "Barnaby Rudge"

17. Tim Linkinwater.

18. Mary Graham.

19. "Dombey and Son"

20. False. "The Pickwick Papers".

21. "Nicholas Nickleby".

22. Little Em'ly.

23. "Bleak House".

24. Mrs. Corney.

25. Pip and Estella.

26. David Copperfield and Dora.

27. Edwin Leeford's sister.

28. Mr. Weller senior.

1. "A Christmas Carol"

2. David Copperfield.

3. Amy and Fanny.

4. She is his aunt

5. Grandfather.

6. c) Agnes.

7. Magwitch's.

8. Uncle and nephew.

9. The Micawber Family   -   "David Copperfield"

    The Barnacle Family   -   "Little Dorrit"

    The Gradgrind Family" -   "Hard Times"

10. "Nicholas Nickleby"

11. True.

12 c) Florence

13. Mrs. Bagnet's

14. "David Copperfield"

15. True.

16. Scrooge.

17. Father and daughter.

18. Oliver Twist

19. Godfather.

20. Helena and Neville.

21. "David Copperfield".

22. The Varden Family   -   "Barnaby Rudge"

    Mr. and Mrs. Fezziwigg   -   "A Christmas Carol"

    Tom and Ruth Pinch   -   "Martin Chuzzlewit"

23. Pip ("Great Expectations")

24. Uncle and niece.

25. "Martin Chuzzlewit".

26. Mrs. Micawber.

27. "The Pickwick Papers"

28. The Pocket family.

ANSWERS: OLIVER TWIST

1.   In a workhouse.

2.   He was named in alphabetical order by Mr. Bumble.

3.   Mr. Bumble.

4.   b) Mrs. Bedwin.

5.   Mr. Sowerberry - Undertaker;

     Mr. Fang - Magistrate;

     Mr. Losberne - Doctor.

6.   Agnes Fleming and Edwin Leeford.

7.   False. Mrs. Corney.

8.   Charley Bates   -   pickpocket;

     Mr. Grimwig   -   friend of Mr. Brownlow's;

     Duff   -   policeman.

9.   An old friend.

10. Noah Claypole.

11. Mr. Gamfield is a chimney sweep,

     Mr. Giles is a butler.

12. Mr. Brownlow.

13. Jack Dawkins.

14. Bet and Nancy.

15. Half brother.

16. Fagin's.

17. Edward Leeford.

18. Bill Sikes.

19. She is killed by Bill Sikes.

20. Rose Fleming.

21. Aunt.

22. Bill Sikes.

23. Mrs. Maylie's.

24. True.

25. Mr. Brownlow.

1. Philip Pirrip.
    He could not pronounce his name properly.

2. A convict. In a churchyard.

3. His sister and her husband, Joe Gargery.

4. Tar-water.

5. Miss Havisham.

6. Twenty minutes to nine.

7. Her birthday.

8. True.

9. Estella.

10. Jaggers   -   a lawyer;

    Herbert Pocket   -   a friend of Pip's;

    Compeyson   -   Magwitch's ex-partner in crime.

11. Abel.

12. Miss Havisham to Estella.

13. Jaggers.

14. Compeyson.

15. Magwitch.

16. She has been adopted by Miss Havisham.

17. Orlick.

18. a) Dolge.

19. Herbert Pocket.

20. London.

21. Orlick.

22. Uncle.

23. Miss Havisham is speaking about Estella.

24. Australia.

25. Orlick.

26. Bentley.

27. Miss Havisham.

28. Compeyson.

29. Herbert Pocket and Startop.

30. Magwitch.

ANSWERS: GREAT EXPECTATIONS

31. He is sentenced to death but dies in prison.

32. Herbert Pocket and his wife.

33. Satis House.

ANSWERS: DAVID COPPERFIELD

1. David's nurse.

2. True.

3. Mr. Murdstone, David's step father.

4. It is a boat.

5. Mr. Creakle.

6. Steerforth and Traddles.

7. Wilkins.

8. Ham and Little Em'ly.

9. a) Dover.

10. Mr. Peggotty.

11. Dr. Strong's.

12. Lawyer.

13. False. Mr. Wickfield's

14. a) Clara
    b) Dan
    c) Tommy/Thomas
    d) James.

15. Uriah Heep.

16. Mr. Wickfield.

17. He is clerk to Mr. Wickfield.

18. Mrs. Heep.

19. Mr. Dick.

20. Miss Betsey calls David "Trotwood";
    Steerforth calls him "Daisy".

21. Peggotty.

22. Ham and Little Em'ly.

23. Steerforth.

24. Mr. Spenlow's. Dora.

25. a) Little Em'ly
    b) Agnes
    c) Dora.

26. They both die.

27. True.

ANSWERS: DAVID COPPERFIELD

28. Miss Mowcher.

29. a) legal.

30. Uriah Heep.

31. Australia.